VOCAL SCORE

From the
Bavarian Highlands

SIX CHORAL SONGS

(SATB)

with piano accompaniment by

EDWARD ELGAR

Op. 27

Words from Bavarian Volkslieder and Schnadahupfler
adapted by

C. ALICE ELGAR

<table>
<tr><td>I.</td><td>The Dance</td><td>III.</td><td>Lullaby</td><td>V.</td><td>On the Alm</td></tr>
<tr><td>II.</td><td>False Love</td><td>IV.</td><td>Aspiration</td><td>VI.</td><td>The Marksmen</td></tr>
</table>

ORCHESTRAL PARTS AVAILABLE FOR HIRE

STAINER & BELL LTD

23 Gruneisen Road, London N3 1DZ

I. THE DANCE

Come and hasten to the dancing,
Merry eyes will soon be glancing,
Ha! my heart upbounds!
Come and dance a merry measure,
Quaff the bright brown ale my treasure,
Hark! what joyous sounds!

Sweet-heart come, on let us haste,
On, on, no time let us waste,
With my heart I love thee!
Dance, dance, for rest we disdain,
Turn, twirl and spin round again,
With my arm I hold thee!

Down the path the lights are gleaming,
Friendly faces gladly beaming
Welcome us with song.
Dancing makes the heart grow lighter,
Makes the world and life grow brighter
As we dance along!

I. THE DANCE

Edward Elgar
Op. 27, No. 1

II. FALSE LOVE

Now we hear the Spring's sweet voice
Singing gladly thro' the world;
Bidding all the earth rejoice.

All is merry in the field,
Flowers grow amid the grass,
Blossoms blue, red, white they yield.

As I seek my maiden true,
Sings the little lark on high
Fain to send her praises due.

As I climb and reach her door,
Ah! I see a rival there,
So farewell for evermore!

Ever true was I to thee,
Never grieved or vexed thee, love,
False, oh! false, art thou to me.

Now amid the forest green,
Far from cruel eyes that mock
Will I dwell unloved, unseen.

II. FALSE LOVE

Edward Elgar
Op. 27, No. 2

III. LULLABY

Sleep, my son, oh! slumber softly,
While thy mother watches o'er thee,
Nothing can affright or harm thee.
Oh! sleep, my son.

> Far-away
> Zithers play,
> Dancing gay,
> Calls today.

> Vainly play
> Zithers gay,
> Here I stay
> All the day.

> Happily
> Guarding thee,
> Peacefully
> Watching thee.

Sleep, my son, oh! slumber softly,
While thy mother watches o'er thee,
Oh! sleep, my son.

III. LULLABY

Edward Elgar
Op. 27, No. 3

IV. ASPIRATION

Over the heights the snow lies deep,
Sunk is the land in peaceful sleep;
Here by the house of God we pray,
Lead, Lord, our souls today.

Shielding, like the silent snow,
Fall His mercies here below.

Calmly then, like the snow-bound land,
Rest we in His protecting hand:
Bowing, we wait His mighty will,
Lead, Lord, and guide us still.

IV. ASPIRATION

Edward Elgar
Op. 27, No. 4

V. ON THE ALM

A mellow bell peals near,
It has so sweet a sound;
I know a maiden dear
With voice as full and round.

A sunlit alm shines clear,
With clover blossoms sweet;
There dwells my maiden dear
And there my love I meet.

There flying with no fear
The swallows pass all day,
And fast, my maiden dear,
Sees chamois haste away.

I cannot linger here,
I cannot wait below;
To seek my maiden dear,
I, to the alm, must go.

The mountain's call I hear,
And up the height I bound;
I know my maiden dear
Will mark my Juchhé* sound.

Rejoicing come I here
My flaxen-haired sweet-heart;
I love thee, maiden dear,
Nay! bid me not depart!

* A yodelling sound. The variant spelling in the underlay is Elgar's simplification for singing purposes.

V. ON THE ALM*

Edward Elgar
Op. 27, No. 5

Allegro piacevole

PIANO

mf legato

sf

f

pp

dim.

SOPRANO

ALTO

TENOR *p*

A mel - low bell peals near, _____ It has _____ so sweet a sound; _____

BASS *p*

A mel - low bell peals near, _____ It has _____ so sweet a sound; _____

p Voices

*A high mountain pasture

I know a mai-den dear With voice as full and

I know a mai-den dear With voice as full and

Ah!

round.

round.

Ah!

con Ped.

Ped.

VI. THE MARKSMEN

Come from the mountain side,
Come from the valleys wide,
See, how we muster strong,
Tramping along!

Rifle on shoulder sling,
Powder and bullets bring,
Manly in mind and heart,
Play we our part.

Sure be each eye today,
Steady each hand must stay,
If in the trial we
Victors would be!

Sharp is the crack! 'tis done!
Lost is the chance, or won;
Right in the gold is it?
Huzza! the hit!

The sun will sink and light the west
And touch the peaks with crimson glow;
Then shadows fill the vale with rest
While stars look peace on all below.

In triumph then we take our way,
And with our prizes homeward wend;
Through meadows sweet with new-mown hay,
A song exultant will we send.

VI. THE MARKSMEN

Edward Elgar
Op. 27, No. 6

Printed in Great Britain by Caligraving Limited